13.25

70 YEARS OF POPULAR MUSIC

THE·EIGHTIES

PART ONE

C000026070

Agadoo, 2
Arthur's Theme (Best That You Can Do), 6
Ben, 9
Cherish, 12
Classic, 15
Easy Lover, 20
Endless Love, 24
Every Time You Go Away, 28
Flashdance…What A Feeling, 32
Ghostbusters, 37
Heartbreaker, 44
Hello, 50
Hill Street Blues, 53
I Could Be So Good For You, 56
I'll Find My Way Home, 61
Invisible, 64
It's My Turn, 68
I Want To Know What Love Is, 74
Just When I Needed You Most, 78
Lady, 86
Let's Hear It For The Boy, 81
Love On The Rocks, 90
Love Theme From The Thorn Birds, 95
Maggie (When You And I Were Young), 98
Move Closer, 101
Nobody Told Me, 104
Sad Songs (Say So Much), 114
Stuck On You, 109
Theme From Cheers (Where Everybody Knows Your Name), 118
The Thorn Birds Theme, 122
Too Late For Goodbyes, 124
Tonight, I Celebrate My Love, 128
Up Where We Belong, 132
We've Got Tonight, 136
What's Love Got To Do With It, 141
Why, 143
The Wind Beneath My Wings, 147
A Winter's Tale, 152
Woman, 155
Woman In Love, 158

WARNER BROS/IMP
First published 1985 © International Music Publications
Exclusive Distributors: International Music Publications, Southend Road, Woodford Green, Essex IG8 8HN, England
252-2-13, Order Ref: 16005, ISBN 0.86359.282.1
Photocopying of this copyright material is illegal.
Cover design by Howard Brown/Peter Wood. Photography by Peter Wood.
Editor: Peter Foss.

AGADOO

Words & Music by M SYMILE,
M DELANCERY and J PERAM

I met a Hu-la mis—tress somewhere in Wai-ki-ki—Where she was sell-ing pine-
F C7
-ap-ple Play-ing uk-u-le-le—And when I went to the girl—"Come on and
F
teach me to sway,"—She laughed and whis-pered to me—"Yes, come to-night to the bay."—
C C7 F
—The love-ly beach and the sky— The moon of Ha-waii—The rum, ca-lyp-so, sa-rong—
B♭ F G7
—Will all be sing-ing this song.— A - ga - doo, doo,
C C6 F

4

5

ARTHUR'S THEME (Best That You Can Do)

Words & Music by BURT BACHARACH, CAROLE BAYER SAGER,
CHRISTOPHER CROSS and PETER ALLEN

BEN

Words & Music by
DON BLACK and WALTER SCHARF

Ben, the two of us need look no more, we both found what we were look-ing for, with a friend to call my own, I'll ne-ver be a-lone, and you, my friend, will see you've got a friend in me.

10

CHERISH

Words & Music by ROBERT BELL,
JAMES TAYLOR and KOOL & THE GANG

Moderately

14

CLASSIC

Words and Music
by ADRIAN GURVITZ

EASY LOVER

Words by PHIL COLLINS
Music by PHILIP BAILEY,
PHIL COLLINS and NATHAN EAST

Easy lover. She'll get a hold on you, believe it,

© 1984 Phil Collins Ltd/Hit and Run (Publishing) Ltd
Pun Music Inc/Sir and Trini Music and New East Music
Warner Bros Music Ltd, 17 Berners Street, London W1P 3DD

ENDLESS LOVE

Words & Music by
LIONEL RICHIE

EVERY TIME YOU GO AWAY

Words and Music
by DARYL HALL

FLASHDANCE . . . WHAT A FEELING

Words by KEITH FORSEY and IRENE CARA
Music by GIORGIO MORODER

GHOSTBUSTERS

Words and Music
by RAY PARKER JR

42

I hear it likes the gals...

I ain't 'fraid__ of no ghost!

E7   E/A

D.S. al Coda I

Yeah,   yeah,   yeah,   yeah.

Coda I   N.C.

(2nd time) Let me tell ya some-thing,

8va b   *8va b*

Chorus 2:
Who you gonna call? (Ghostbusters!)
You've had a dose of a freaky ghost, baby; you better call Ghostbusters.

Verse 3:
Don't get caught alone, oh no! (Ghostbusters!)
When it comes through your door,
Unless you just want some more, I think you better call Ghostbusters.

HEARTBREAKER

Words & Music by
BARRY, ROBIN and MAURICE GIBB

I have to say it and it's hard for me,— You got me cry-in' like I

thought I would never be. Love is be-lievin' but you let me down— How can I love you when you

49

HELLO

Words and Music
by LIONEL RICHIE

* Recorded version has G# in bass.

know just what to say___ and you know just what to do___ And I
how to win your heart___ for I have-n't got a clue___ But

want to tell___ you so much, I love you...
let me start___ by say-ing, I love you...

2. I
3. *Inst.*

you.

rall.

HILL STREET BLUES

By MIKE POST

I COULD BE SO GOOD FOR YOU

Words & Music by
PATRICIA WATERMAN and GERARD KENNY

I'LL FIND MY WAY HOME

Words & Music by
J ANDERSON and VANGELIS

62

(MIDDLE)

spi - rit is lost___   how will I

find what is near.___   Don't ques-tion I'm not a - lone___

some-how I'll find my way home.___   2. My sun shall

Verse 2: My sun shall rise in the east,
So shall my heart be at peace,
And if you're asking me when
I'll say it starts at the end.

Middle: You know your will to be free
Is matched with love secretly
And talk would alter your prayer
Somehow you find you are there.

Verse 3: Your friend is close by your side
And speaks in far ancient tongue
A season's wish will come true
All seasons begin with you.
One world we

63

Verse & Chorus: (Repeat)

Verse 1: (Repeat)

Chorus: Spirit is strong, I know it can't be wrong
No questions I'm not alone.
Somehow I'll find my way home (x 4)

INVISIBLE

Words and Music
by LAMONT DOZIER

IT'S MY TURN

Words by CAROLE BAYER SAGER
Music by MICHAEL MASSER

I can't cov-er up my feel-ings in the name of love, Or play-ing safe, for a while that was eas-y; And if liv-ing for my-self is what I'm guilt-y of, Go on and sen-tence me, I'll still be free. It's my turn to see what I can see. I hope you'll un-der-stand

71

dam-age that's been done And now it's my turn to reach and touch the sky.

No one's gon-na say At least I did-n't try. It's my— turn,——

—— Yes, it's my ——— turn, ———

Fade on repeat

It's my— turn, ——— My— turn.

I WANT TO KNOW WHAT LOVE IS

Words and Music
by MICK JONES

Moderately

I've got-ta take a lit-tle time,

a lit-tle time to think things o-ver.

I bet-ter read be-tween the lines,____ in case I
need it when I'm old - er.____

Now, this moun-tain I____ must climb____ feels like the world up-on____ my shoul-
I'm gon-na take a lit-tle time,____ a lit-tle time to look a-round____

JUST WHEN I NEEDED YOU MOST

Words and Music
by RANDY VANWARMER

Left. me _ just when I need-ed you most. _ 3. Now

D.%. al Coda CODA

You

Verse 1: Repeat.

Verse 6: Now I love you more than I loved you before,
And now where I'll find comfort, God knows
'Cause you left me, just when I need you most,
Oh yea, you left me, just when I needed you
Most, you left me, just when I needed you most.

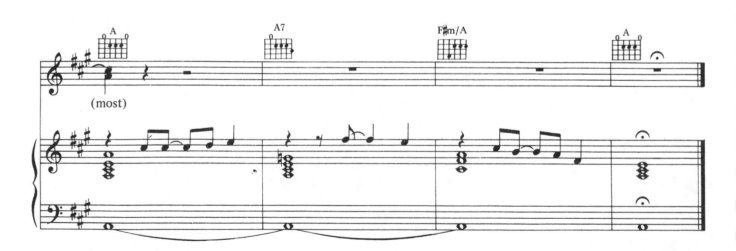

(most)

LET'S HEAR IT FOR THE BOY

Moderately bright ♩ = 120

Words by TOM SNOW
Music by DEAN PITCHFORD

1. My ba - by, he don't talk
2. (See additional lyrics)

sweet; — he ain't got much to say. _____ But he

loves me, loves me, loves _ me; I know that he loves me an -

wo,   let's hear it   for the boy. —

2. My

Instrumental solo ad lib.

Verse 2:
My baby may not be rich;
He's watchin' ev'ry dime.
But he loves me, loves me, loves me.
We always have a real good time.
And maybe he sings off key,
But that's all right by me, yeah.
But what he does, he does so well.
Makes me wanna yell.

(To Chorus:)

LADY

Words and Music
by LIONEL RICHIE

* Recorded 1/2 step higher, in E♭ minor

LOVE ON THE ROCKS

Words & Music by
NEIL DIAMOND and GILBERT BECAUD

LOVE THEME FROM THE THORN BIRDS

By HENRY MANCINI

MAGGIE (When You And I Were Young)

Words by G W JOHNSON
Music by J A BUTTERFIELD
Arranged by MICK FOSTER,
TONY ALLEN and DONIE CASSIDY

MOVE CLOSER

Words and Music
by PHYLLIS NELSON

spoken:
Hey baby, you go your way and I'll go mine, but in the meantime

When we're to-geth - er touch - ing each oth -
So when I say____ sug - ar____ and I whisp - er I love____

NOBODY TOLD ME

Words and Music
by JOHN LENNON

108

STUCK ON YOU

Words and Music
by LIONEL RICHIE

Might - y glad you stayed
Might - y glad you stayed

Oh, I'm leav - ing on that mid - night train to - mor-

more rhythmically

SAD SONGS (Say So Much)

Words & Music by
ELTON JOHN and BERNIE TAUPIN

Moderately

Guess there are times ___ when we ___ all ___ need ___ to share ___ a lit-
suf - fer - ing ___ e - nough ___ oh ___ to write ___

- tle pain, ___ and iron-ing out the rough spots ___
___ it down, ___ when ev - 'ry sing - le word makes sense, ___

THEME FROM CHEERS (Where Everybody Knows Your Name)

Words & Music by
GARY PORTNOY and JUDY HART ANGELO

1. Mak - ing your way in the world to - day takes ev - 'ry - thing you've got.
2.3. (See additional lyrics)

Tak - ing a break from all your wor - ries sure would help a lot.

Would-n't you like to get a - way?

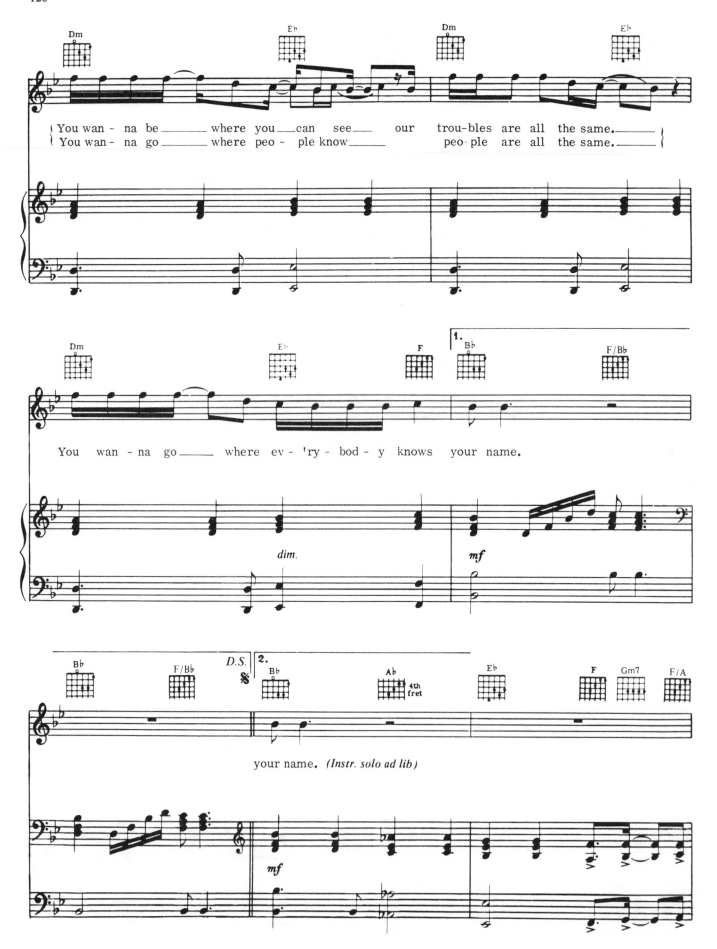

Verse 2: All those nights
When you've got no lights;
The check is in the mail.
And your little angel
Hung the cat up by its tail.
And your third fiancee didn't show.
Sometimes you wanna go . . .
(To Chorus:)

Verse 3: Roll out of bed;
Mr. Coffee's dead.
The morning's looking bright.
And your shrink ran off to Europe
And didn't even write.
And your husband wants to be a girl.
Be glad there's one place in the world. . . . .
(To Chorus:)

THE THORN BIRDS THEME

By HENRY MANCINI

TOO LATE FOR GOODBYES

Words and Music
BY JULIAN LENNON

TONIGHT, I CELEBRATE MY LOVE

Words & Music by
MICHAEL MASSER and GERRY GOFFIN

night   no one's gon - na   find__ us,___   we'll leave the world_ be -
night   our spir - its will be climb - ing___   to a sky lit up__ with

hind__ us,___   when I make love to you.___   2. To-
dia - monds___   when I make

love to you___   to - night.

To - love to you.___   To-

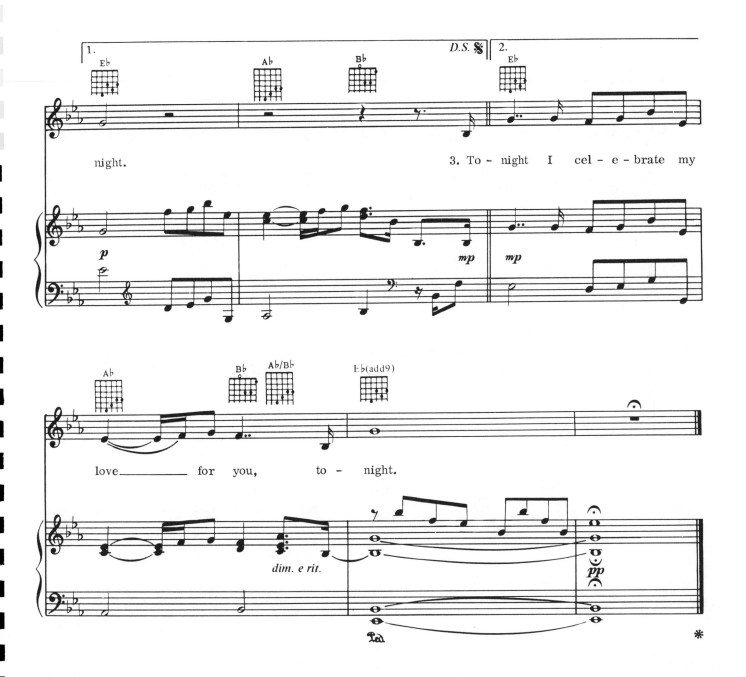

Verse 3:
Tonight I celebrate my love for you,
And soon this old world will seem brand new.
Tonight we will both discover
How friends turn into lovers,
When I make love to you.
(To Chorus:)

UP WHERE WE BELONG

Words by
WILL JENNINGS

Words by WILL JENNINGS
Music by BUFFY SAINTE-MARIE and JACK NITZSCHE

1. Who knows what to-mor-row brings;___ in a world, few hearts sur-
2. *(See additional lyrics)*

-vive? All I know is the way I feel;___ when it's

real, I keep it a-live.___ The

Verse 2:
Some hang on to "used-to-be",
Live their lives looking behind.
All we have is here and now;
All our life, out there to find.
The road is long.
There are mountains in our way,
But we climb them a step every day.

WE'VE GOT TONIGHT

Words and Music
by BOB SEGER

WHAT'S LOVE GOT TO DO WITH IT

Words & Music by
GRAHAM LYLE and TERRY BRITTEN

WHY

Words & Music by
NILE RODGERS and BERNARD EDWARDS

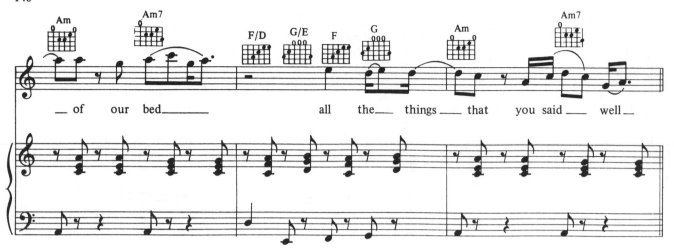

_ of our bed_____ all the__ things __ that you said __ well__

Intro & Chorus: *(Repeat)*

Verse 2:
You say our love was sacred
But you left me alone to make it
You want to come back again some day
But darling here's what I say.

Intro: *(Repeat)*

Chorus:
(6 bars only)
Why does your love hurt so much, why?
Why does your love hurt so much?

BRIDGE

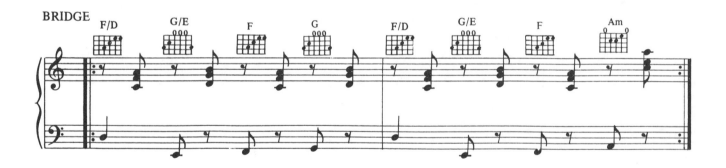

Intro: (Repeat) + Why why does your love hurt so much
You say you'll come back
Again some day but darling
Here's what I say,
La de da de da . . .
Why does your love hurt so much
Don't know why . . . . *(etc, to fade)*

THE WIND BENEATH MY WINGS

Words & Music by
LARRY HENLEY and JEFF SILBAR

'cause you are the wind___ be-neath my wings.

It might have ap-peared___ to go un-

no - ticed that I've got it all___ here in my

heart.

I want you to know___ I know the

A WINTER'S TALE

Music by MIKE BATT
Words by MIKE BATT and TIM RICE

The

nights are cold - er now, maybe I should close the door,
while I stand a - lone a bell is ring - ing far a - way;

and an - y - way the snow has cov - ered all your
I won - der if you hear, I won - der if you're

foot - steps and I can fol - low you no more. The fire still burns at
listen - ing, I won - der where you are to - day? Good luck! I wish you

world - wide scale___ we're just an - oth - er win - ter's ___ tale.

tale. It was

world wide scale___ we're just an - oth - er win - ter's ___ tale.

WOMAN

Words and Music
by JOHN LENNON

WOMAN IN LOVE

Words & Music by
BARRY and ROBIN GIBB

Life is a mo-ment in space,—
With you e-ter-nal-ly mine,—
when the dream is gone —— it's a lone-li-er place.——
in love there is —— no meas-ure of time.——
I kiss the morn-ing good - bye,—— but down in - side——
We planned it all at the start,—— that you and I——

Printed in Great Britain by
St Edmundsbury Press Limited, Bury St Edmunds, Suffolk